Tom and Ricky

and the

Mystery in Room 512

Bob Wright

High Noon Books
Novato, California

Mystery in Room 512

Bob Wright
AR B.L.: 2.4
Points: 0.5   UG

Cover Design: Nancy Peach
Interior Illustrations: Herb Heidinger

Glossary: happen, believe, million, package, hotel, present, diamonds

International Standard Book Number: 0-87879-359-3

9 8 7 6 5 4
5 4 3 2 1 0 9 8

You'll enjoy all the High Noon Books. Write for
a free full list of titles.

Contents

CHAPTER 1

The Package

Tom and Ricky were on their way home. They had just been to a movie. Now, they were riding the bus home.

"I didn't like that movie," Ricky said.

"Why?" Tom asked.

"Who could believe a story like that? Things like that don't happen in real life. That movie was hard to believe," Ricky said.

"Well, I believed it," Tom said.

"Well, I didn't!" Ricky laughed.

"What if something like that happened to us?" Tom asked his friend.

"What do you mean?" Ricky said.

"The movie was about two boys who find a million dollars. What if that happened to us?" Tom said.

Ricky laughed again. Then he said, "No one would believe it. I wouldn't believe it. Things like that only happen in the movies."

"But what if we *did* find a lot of money?" Tom said.

"Ask me then!" his friend answered.

"It *could* happen," Tom said.

"Oh sure . . . Anything *could* happen. But don't count on it," Ricky answered.

A man was sitting near Tom and Ricky. He had a package on the seat by him. The man seemed to be mad.

All of a sudden the man got up. He walked to the door of the bus. He got off at the next stop. He left the package on the seat.

Tom saw what had happened. "Ricky! That man left his package," he said.

"I bet he forgot it," Ricky said.

Tom picked up the package. He started for the door of the bus.

"Where are you going?" Ricky asked.

"Let's get off here. We have to give the man his package. We can walk the rest of the way home," Tom said.

3

The two boys got off the bus. They ran down the street. They were looking for the man who had lost his package.

"There he is!" Ricky said.

Tom and Ricky ran after the man.

"Wait! Here is your package," Tom yelled.

The man did not seem to hear Tom. He kept on walking. He did not turn to look around.

"I have your package!" Ricky yelled.

But the man still would not stop. He began to walk faster. At the next corner, he turned and was gone.

The boys ran to the corner. They could not see the man. "Where did he go?" Ricky asked.

"I don't know," Tom answered.

Just then, Ricky saw the man. He was about to go into a small hotel. He had a hotel key in his hand.

The boys ran up to the man. Tom showed him the package. "You left this on the bus," he said to the man.

The man looked at the package. "What are you talking about? That package is not mine. Go away! Leave me alone!" he said.

The man opened the door of the hotel and went inside.

CHAPTER 2

A Surprise

Tom and Ricky looked at each other. They were surprised. They didn't know what to do next.

"That was *his* package! Why wouldn't he take it?" Ricky said.

"I don't know. I saw him leave it on the seat. It *must* be his package," Tom said.

"But he said that it was not his. Maybe we were wrong," Ricky said.

"Maybe the package was on the seat before the man got on the bus," Tom said.

"So what should we do with the package now?" Ricky asked.

"I'm not sure," Tom answered.

"Let's go home and think about it," Ricky said.

The boys walked the rest of the way home. They went to Ricky's house. Ricky opened the door and they went inside.

Ricky's dog Patches was happy to see them. The dog barked and wagged his tail. Then he looked at the package.

"Patches thinks we brought him a present," Tom said.

"No, Patches. This is not for you," Ricky said to his dog.

Tom and Ricky looked at the package. It was not very big. It was covered with dark brown paper.

Ricky turned the package over in his hands. There was no writing on it. There was nothing at all on it.

"What do you think is inside?" Tom asked.

"Who knows?" Ricky answered.

"Let's open it," Tom said.

"Do you think we should?" Ricky asked.

"We might find out who owns it," Tom said.

"OK. Let's see," Ricky answered. He took off the brown paper.

They both looked at the package. They couldn't believe what they saw.

"Look at that!" Ricky said.

There was money inside the package. It was more money than the boys had ever seen.

"It looks like a million dollars!"

"It looks like a million dollars!" Tom said.

"Why would anyone leave all that money on a bus?" Ricky said.

"Maybe it isn't real," Tom said.

"It sure *looks* real," Ricky answered.

Ricky took some money from the top of the pile of money. He looked at it closely.

"Is it real?" Tom asked.

"I think so. But we have to make sure," Ricky answered.

"Come on. Let's take some of it to the bank. They can tell us if it is real," Ricky said.

They left the rest of the money on the table. They ran out the door. Ricky was in such a hurry that he even forgot to close the door.

10

CHAPTER 3

A Hard Story to Believe

The boys ran all the way to the bank. They went inside. A woman who worked there said, "May I help you?"

Ricky took the money from his coat. He showed it to the woman. "Is this real money?" he asked her.

The woman looked at the money. She held it up to the light. Then she handed it back to Ricky. "Yes, it is real," she said.

"Thank you," Ricky said to the woman.

Then he turned and started to leave. "Come on, Tom. Let's get back home. We have to find out who owns that money," he said.

They ran back to Ricky's house. The door was still open. "You forgot to close the door when we left," Tom said.

"You're right. I was thinking about all that money. But we weren't gone that long," Ricky said.

The boys went inside. Then Ricky stopped. He looked at the table. "The money is gone! Someone has taken it!" he said.

"Maybe Patches took it. You know how he likes to hide things." Tom said.

Ricky called his dog. "Patches! Come here!"

Patches came running in. There was dirt all over him. The dog had been in the back yard.

"Patches! What have you done with the money? Did you hide it?" Ricky said.

Patches barked. He wagged his tail. Then he started for the open door. He went out into the back yard.

Tom and Ricky were right in back of him. Patches led them to where he had been digging.

Both boys started to push the dirt away.

"He *did* hide it!" Ricky said.

But there was no money. There was just a bone.

"If Patches didn't take the money, who did?" Tom asked.

13

"I don't know. Someone else must have taken it," Ricky answered.

"Who could it be?" Tom asked.

"I left the door open when we went to the bank. Someone took the money when we left," Ricky said.

"But we weren't gone that long," Tom said.

"Someone saw us get off the bus. Someone knew there was money in the package," Ricky said.

"Let's call Sergeant Collins. He will know what to do," Tom said.

Ricky made a telephone call to Sergeant Collins. The policeman said that he would be right over.

Sergeant Collins was there right away. The boys told him their story.

The policeman looked around the house. He couldn't find any of the money. Even the brown paper on the package was gone.

Sergeant Collins shook his head. "I would like to believe you, boys. But your story is hard to believe. Is this some kind of a joke?" he said.

CHAPTER 4

The Man in the Wheel Chair

"It's no joke, Sergeant Collins. We really did find a package full of money," Ricky said.

"Just like the boys in the movie," Tom added.

"What movie?" the policeman asked.

Tom told him about the movie they had seen. "We went to a movie. In the movie, these two boys found a lot of money. Then we did, too, on the bus home," he said.

Sergeant Collins just looked at them.

"Don't you believe us?" Ricky said.

Ricky showed the policeman the money he had taken to the bank. "This is part of the money. And there was a lot more," he said.

Sergeant Collins looked at the money. But he still was not sure.

Sergeant Collins looked at the money. But he still was not sure.

Then Ricky said, "Come with us to that hotel. We will find the man who left the package. He knows we found that package."

"We are not making this up," Tom said.

Sergeant Collins said, "All right. Let's go to that hotel. But how are you going to find that man? There are a lot of people staying in the hotel."

Ricky thought about it. Then he said, "The man had a key in his hand when we stopped him. The key said Room 512. Yes, it was Room 512. I know that for sure!"

"Let's go!" the policeman said.

They got in Sergeant Collins' car. They got to the hotel very fast. Then they went up to Room 512.

"Who is it?" a man's voice said.

"The police," Sergeant Collins answered.

They waited. Then Sergeant Collins said, "Open the door. I'd like to talk to you."

The door opened. There was a man in a wheel chair. "What is it?" the man said.

Sergeant Collins told the man about Tom and Ricky's story. "The boys said that you left a package full of money on the bus," the policeman said to the man.

The man seemed mad. He just looked at Sergeant Collins.

Then he said, "How could that be? I am in a wheel chair. I can't ride on a bus. I have never seen those boys."

"Yes, you have!" Tom yelled.

"I don't know anything about a package full of money. I don't know what you're talking about. Leave me alone!" the man said.

Sergeant Collins seemed to believe the man. He turned to Ricky and Tom. "Come on, boys. Let's go."

CHAPTER 5

At the Hotel

Tom, Ricky, and Sergeant Collins left the man alone. They went out of the hotel.

"I'm mixed up," Sergeant Collins said.

"What do you mean?" Ricky asked.

"That man is in a wheel chair. How could he have been on that bus? Why would he leave a package of money on a bus? Are you sure that's the same man?" Sergeant Collins asked.

"That's the man," Ricky said.

"But he wasn't in a wheel chair," Tom said.

"You said you found a big package of money. No one has said that any money is missing in this town. If that much money was missing, I would have heard about it," the Sergeant said.

"But we did find a package of money," Ricky said.

"And we took some of it to the bank. It is real money," Tom said.

"I need more to go on. This just doesn't add up," Sergeant Collins said.

"What do we do now?" Ricky asked.

"I have to go. Let me know if you find out anything more about all of this," Sergeant Collins said. Then he got into his car and left.

"Now what?" Tom asked.

"I don't know what to do," Ricky said.

"I have an idea. Let's stay here. We don't have to stay a long time. Let's see if that man comes out of the hotel," Tom said.

"That's a good idea. He might have to leave for something," Ricky answered.

"That man in the wheel chair has the answer to all of this. I know he does," Tom said.

Tom and Ricky stayed there a long time. The man didn't come out of the hotel. But a woman did. She looked at them. Then she walked over to them.

Tom and Ricky saw her coming. "Who's that?" Tom asked.

"I don't know. But she seems to know us," Ricky answered.

The woman walked up to them. "Hello," she said.

"Hi. Do you want something?" Ricky asked.

"I want to help you," she answered.

"How can you help us?" Tom asked.

"I work for the man in the wheel chair. He would like to see you boys," she said.

"See us? What for?" Ricky asked.

"He told Sergeant Collins he didn't know us," Tom said.

"He does not want anyone to know who he really is. But he says that it is all right for both of you to know," she said.

"What's going on?" Ricky asked.

"I'll tell you. But don't tell anyone," she said.

"I work for the man in the wheel chair. He would like to see you boys."

"OK," Ricky said.

"That man in the wheel chair is Mr. Rich. And he is very, very rich. He likes to give money away. It makes him happy to do that. That's why he left that package of money for you," she said.

"But why did he tell Sergeant Collins that he didn't leave the money?" Tom asked.

"He doesn't want people to know he does this," she said.

"I don't get any of this," Ricky said.

"Come with me. We'll all go and see Mr. Rich. He will tell you everything," she said.

CHAPTER 6

A Trick

Tom, Ricky, and the woman started to walk back to the hotel. They were still talking.

"I still don't get all of this," Tom said.

"You'll like Mr. Rich. He is a very nice man. He will tell you everything you want to know," the woman said.

"But why was he in a wheel chair?" Ricky asked.

"Oh, that. He does that so people won't know who he is," the woman said.

"You mean he really doesn't have to be in that wheel chair?" Tom asked.

"No, he doesn't," she answered.

"So why does he want to see us?" Tom asked.

"Mr. Rich was sorry to hear that you had lost the money he left for you. He wants to give you another package of money," she said.

"But why did he leave the money for us?" Ricky asked.

"I don't know. Mr. Rich is that way. He picks people he wants to give money to. I just work for him," she said.

"But what about the first package of money?" Tom asked.

"You said someone took it when you went to the bank," the woman said.

"Why didn't Mr. Rich tell Sergeant Collins everything you are telling us?" Ricky asked.

"I told you. Mr. Rich doesn't want a lot of people to know he gives away money. People would come to him and ask for money. He likes to give it to people in his own way. That is why he said he had never seen you," she said.

"Well, here we are. Room 512. Mr. Rich's room," Ricky said.

The woman opened the door, and they all went in.

No one was in the room.

"Where's Mr. Rich?" Ricky asked.

"He's resting in the other room. It's all right. You can go in and see him. He's waiting for you," the woman said.

Tom and Ricky opened the door to the next room.

"It's all right. Go right in," she said.

The room was dark.

"I can't see anything. Can you, Tom?" Ricky asked.

"No. It's too dark. Where's Mr. Rich?" Tom asked.

All of a sudden the door closed. Then they heard the door being locked.

"What's going on?" Ricky asked.

"I don't know," Tom answered.

"I think we've been tricked!" Ricky said. He pulled on the door. It wouldn't open.

"We're locked in this room!" Tom said.

"I think we've been tricked!" Ricky said. He pulled on the door.

Then they heard the woman. "You can't get out of that room. Don't do anything. Don't say anything. You'll be all right. You're not going anywhere."

Then they heard Mr. Rich. "Nice work, June. You really tricked them. Now they are out of the way."

"Why did you leave the money on the bus anyway?" she asked him.

The boys could tell she was mad.

"I told you. I had to get rid of it. I thought the police were after us," he said.

"It was a good thing we weren't sitting together on the bus. I just couldn't believe you would leave that money," she said.

Tom turned to Ricky. "She was on the bus. She saw us go to your house."

"I still don't get what's going on," Ricky said.

"That makes two of us," Tom answered.

CHAPTER 7

Locked In

Ricky and Tom were locked in the room. They didn't move. They wanted to hear what Mr. Rich and June were saying.

"Do you think that the boys know the money is fake?" June said.

"No. They took the top money to the bank to check. That money was real. But all the rest is fake," Mr. Rich answered.

"Be sure to put real money on top before we buy the diamonds," June said.

"I'll do that right now," Mr. Rich said.

"So what's next?" June asked.

"We have to get out of here. I still think that the police are closing in on us. Let's take that fake money and buy those diamonds now," the man answered.

"What about the boys?" June said.

"They are locked in. They cannot get out. By the time anyone finds them, we will be gone," Mr. Rich said to June.

"So what are we waiting for? Let's go to Long's Diamond Store right now," June said.

"Right. Let's do it before the police find out what we are up to," Mr. Rich said.

The boys heard Mr. Rich and June leave.

Ricky hit the door with his hands. "Help! Let us out of here!" he yelled.

"It's no use. No one can hear us," Tom said.

"You're right. We will have to get out of here on our own," Ricky answered.

"And when we do, we have to stop them," Tom said.

"They tricked us. We thought all that money was real. But only the top ones were. They are going to buy diamonds with that fake money," Ricky said.

"But why did the woman trick us into coming up to this room?" Tom asked.

"She saw us waiting outside the hotel," Ricky said.

"Right! She and Mr. Rich knew that we would find out what they were doing. So they had to get us out of the way," Tom said.

"And we *are* out of the way. We have to get out of this room and call Sergeant Collins," Ricky said.

They looked in the dark. There was no telephone to call for help. And the door was locked.

Tom tried kicking the door down. But it was too strong. He could not break it down. "This door is like a stone wall," Tom said.

"Wait! I have an idea!" Ricky said.

"What is it?" Tom asked.

"Let's take the door off," Ricky said.

Ricky looked around for something to use. He found a metal bar. He pulled and pushed. All of a sudden the door fell off.

They were free.

"Now what?" Tom asked.

"Let's call Sergeant Collins. We have to tell him what they are up to," Ricky answered.

There was a telephone in the other room. Ricky called Sergeant Collins right away.

CHAPTER 8

Another Trick

"Hello, Sergeant Collins? This is Ricky. Tom and I have found out what is going on," Ricky said on the telephone.

"What do you mean?" the policeman asked.

"I mean about the missing money. That man in the wheel chair doesn't really need a wheel chair. And he has a woman helping him," Ricky said.

"Slow down! What are you talking about?" Sergeant Collins asked.

Ricky told him everything. He told Sergeant Collins that Mr. Rich and June were on their way to Long's Diamond Store. "They are going to buy real diamonds with fake money. It's a trick. You have to stop them," Ricky said.

"How long ago did they leave the hotel?" Sergeant Collins asked.

"About a half hour ago. They locked us in. We just got out," Ricky said.

"All right. I'll get moving on it," Sergeant Collins said.

Ricky put down the telephone. "Let's go. We can't let them get away."

Long's Diamond Store was on the other side of town. The boys had to take a bus.

"I hope that Sergeant Collins gets there in time," Tom said.

The bus ride took almost half an hour. Finally, they got to Long's Diamond Store. But it seemed that they were too late.

"Look! Mr. Rich and June are leaving the store. They are getting in a car. There they go!" Ricky said.

The boys ran into the store. Mr. Long, the store owner, was there.

"Did you just sell those two people some diamonds?" Tom asked.

"Yes, I did. And they paid me a lot of money for the diamonds," Mr. Long answered.

"That money was fake," Ricky said.

Just then Sergeant Collins walked in.

"What took you so long?" Ricky asked.

"Mr. Rich and June just left," Tom said.

"Yes, I did. And they paid me a lot of money for the diamonds."

"OK, Mr. Long. You can tell them now," the Sergeant said.

"I know about the money," Mr. Long said.

"You do?" Tom asked.

"Yes. Sergeant Collins called me after you called him. I was waiting for Mr. Rich and June. We had to catch them this way," Mr. Long said.

"I got them. They weren't far away," Sergeant Collins said.

"I still don't get who took the money from Ricky's house," Tom said.

"It was June. She saw you go to Ricky's house. She waited. When you went to the bank she went in and took the money," Sergeant Collins said.

"They wanted us out of the way," Ricky said.

"That's right!" Sergeant Collins said.

"They didn't think we would get free and call you," Ricky said to Sergeant Collins.

"Right again. I have them and the fake money. And Mr. Long has his diamonds back," Sergeant Collins said.

"They tried to trick us. But the last trick was on them," Ricky said.